On the Farm

by Jeff Dille

illustrated by Amanda Schaffer

Harcourt

Orlando Boston Dallas Chicago San Diego

www.harcourtschool.com

Cock a doodle do

A rooster on the farm

2

oink
oink

A pig on the farm

neigh
neigh

A horse on the farm

A goose on the farm

moo
moo

A cow on the farm

baa baa

A lamb on the farm

Shhh
shhh

A night on the farm